Zany Picture Riddles

Written & Illustrated by
JOYCE BEHR

Sterling Publishing Co., Inc. New York

Other Books Illustrated by Joyce Behr

Bananas Don't Grow on Trees
Biggest Riddle Book in the World
Calculator Puzzles, Tricks & Games
Daffy Definitions
Doctor Knock-Knock's Official Knock-Knock Dictionary
Funny Insults & Snappy Put-Downs
Gigantic Joke Book
Monster Madness
Polar Bears Like It Hot
Ridiculous Nicholas Pet Riddles
Ridiculous Nicholas Riddle Book
Silly Songbook
Silly Verse (and Even Worse)

Library of Congress Cataloging-in-Publication Data

Behr, Joyce.
[Picture-puzzle riddle book]
Zany picture riddles / written and illustrated by Joyce Behr.
p. cm.
Previously published: Picture-puzzle riddle book. © 1983.
Includes index.
Summary: Hundreds of riddles with answers in rebus form.
ISBN 0-8069-6780-3 (pbk.)
1. Riddles, Juvenile. 2. Rebuses. [1. Riddles. 2. Rebuses.]
I. Title.
[PN6371.5.B38 1988]
818′.5402—dc19 88-1595
CIP
AC

3 5 7 9 10 8 6 4 2

Published in 1988 by Sterling Publishing Co., Inc.
Two Park Avenue, New York, N.Y. 10016
Originally published in hardcover under the title,
"Picture-Puzzle Riddle Book," © 1983 by
Sterling Publishing Co., Inc.
Distributed in Canada by Oak Tree Press Ltd.
℅ Canadian Manda Group, P.O. Box 920, Station U
Toronto, Ontario, Canada M8Z 5P9
Distributed in the United Kingdom by Blandford Press
Link House, West Street, Poole, Dorset BH15 1LL, England
Distributed in Australia by Capricorn Ltd.
P.O. Box 665, Lane Cove, NSW 2066
Manufactured in the United States of America

Sterling ISBN 0-8069-6780-3 Paper

CONTENTS

For Behrs, Behrs,
everywheres!

HOW TO USE THIS BOOK

Before people invented words, they made pictures:

Cave men and women used pictures to communicate ideas:

Later, the Egyptians used picture-symbols called hieroglyphics:

A rebus is a kind of picture-writing using both

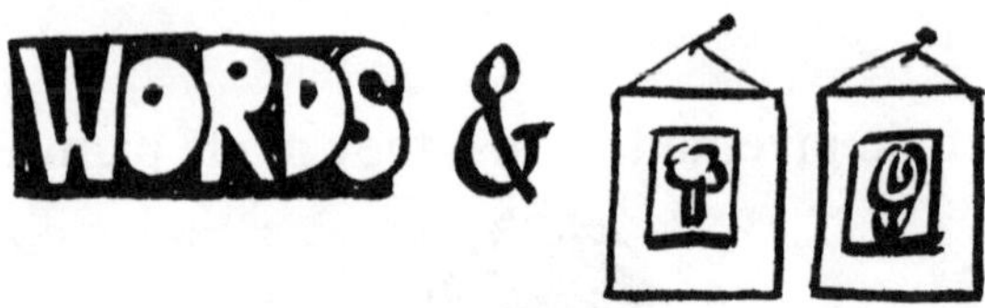

Letters can be added or subtracted with a plus (+) or minus (–) sign. For example:

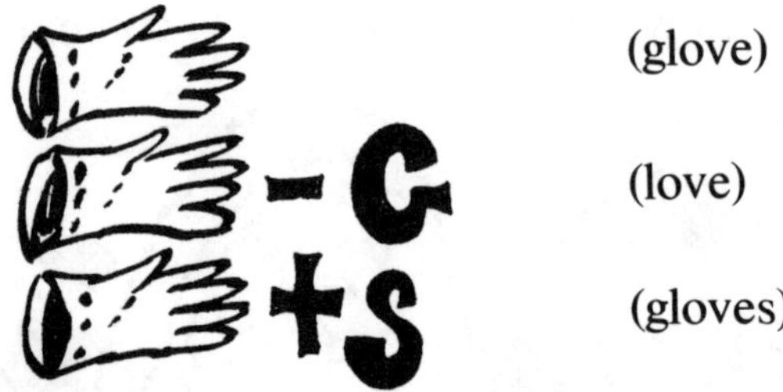

(glove)

(love)

(gloves)

This set of pictures is called a rebus.

In this book every riddle is in words—every answer is a rebus—

except for one

or two

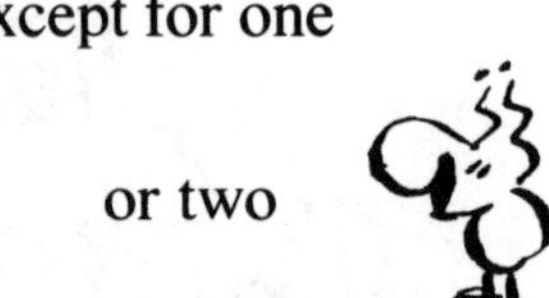

surprises . . .

You can sound out a rebus—sometimes. Sometimes you need to spell it out. If you can't figure out the words, you can find the correct answers printed upside down below each puzzle, so you won't have to

for them.

We think this  will give you some fun riddles and sharpen your wits at the same time.

These picture puzzles are not kid stuff, and doing them in your head doesn't always work. We tried it and had to sneak a

to figure them out.

So get on your

, and

!!

QUICKIES

1.

What did the rope say to the squirrel?

NUTS (KNOTS) TO YOU!

What color is the north wind?

BLUE

What kind of bow can be neither tied nor untied?

A RAINBOW

What flowers do you wear on your face?

TULIPS (TWO LIPS)

Did Adam and Eve have a date?

N

NO! AN APPLE

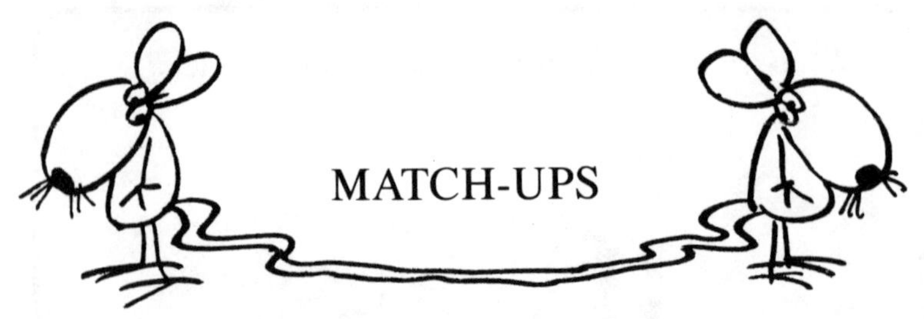

MATCH UP THE RIDDLES (ON THIS PAGE) WITH THEIR ANSWERS (THEY'RE OUT OF ORDER) ON THE NEXT PAGE.

1. How many peas are in a pint?
2. What has a center, but no beginning or end?
3. What has teeth, but no mouth?
4. What has a neck, but no head?
5. What tree do you hold in your hand?

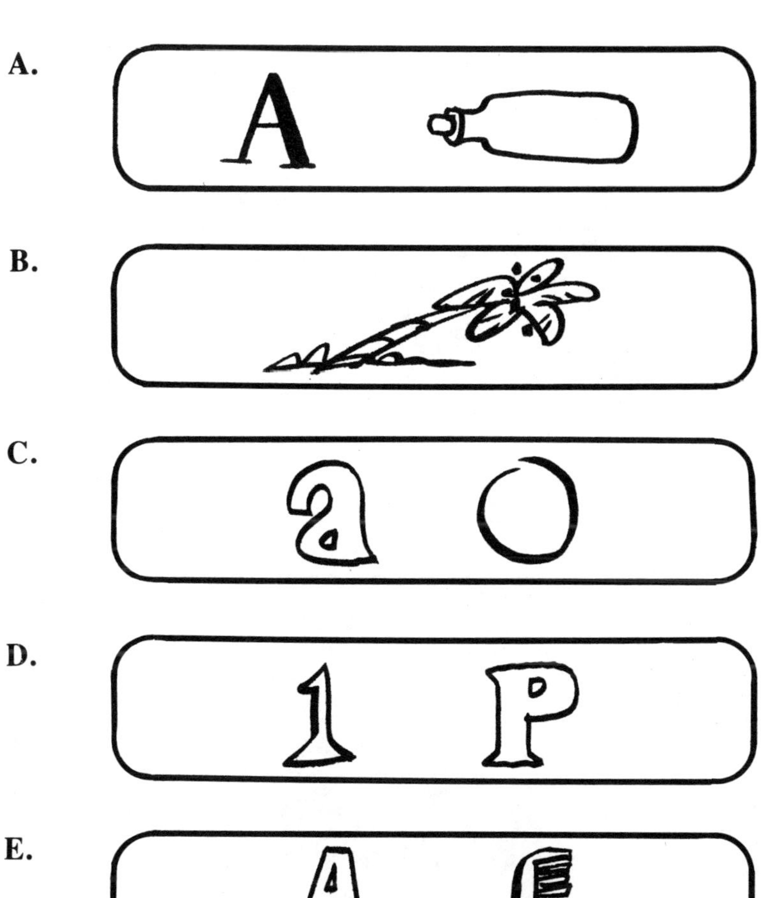

1. D (IP)
2. C (A CIRCLE)
3. E (A COMB)
4. A (A BOTTLE)
5. B (PALM)

What did the mama broom say to the baby broom at bedtime?

"GO TO SWEEP"

What did one banana say to the other banana?

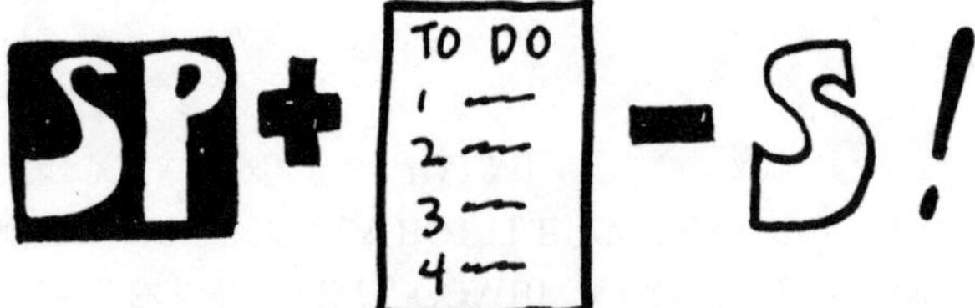

"LET US (LETTUCE) SPLIT!"

What did the mayonnaise say to the refrigerator?

"SHUT THE DOOR—I'M DRESSING!"

What baby is born with whiskers?

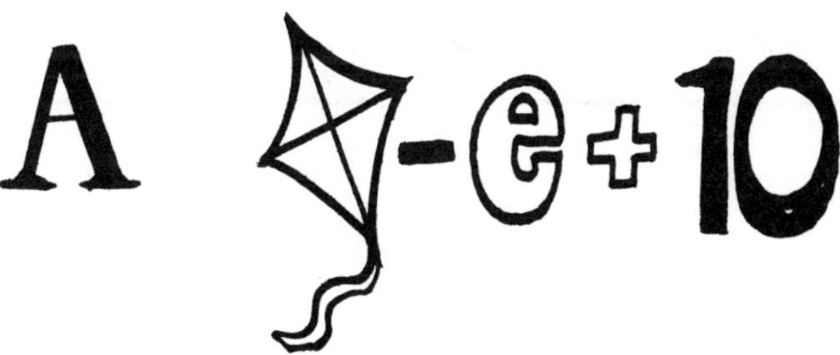

A KITTEN

Why did the ocean roar?

ITS BED WAS WET

HORSE LAUGHS

2.

What do you do at a dude ranch?

HORSE AROUND

What do you say to greet a cow?

"WHAT'S MOO?"

Why didn't you hear about the 300 cows that disappeared?

NOBODY'S HEARD (HERD)

Why do cows wear bells?

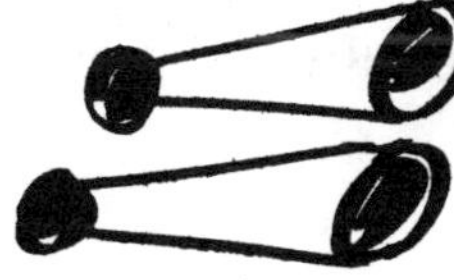

○○○ BECAUSE○THEIR○HORNS○DON'T○WORK ○○○

MATCH-UPS

MATCH UP THE RIDDLES (ON THIS PAGE) WITH THEIR ANSWERS (THEY'RE OUT OF ORDER) ON THE NEXT PAGE.

1. Who always goes to sleep with his shoes on?

2. What is as big as a hippopotamus but doesn't weigh an ounce?

3. What weighs almost nothing but cannot be lifted?

4. What runs around the cow pasture but never moves?

5. What makes more noise than a pig caught under a fence?

A.

B.

C.

D.

E.

1. ○○○○○○○○○○○○ D (A HORSE) ○○○○○○○○○○○○○○
2. ○○○○○ C (A HIPPOPOTAMUS'S SHADOW) ○○○○○○○
3. ○○○○○○○○○○○○ A (A BUBBLE) ○○○○○○○○○○○○○
4. ○○○○○○○○○○○○ E (THE FENCE) ○○○○○○○○○○○○○
5. ○○ B (TWO PIGS CAUGHT UNDER A FENCE) ○○○

Why did the horse sneeze?

It

-t+d

a

LITTLE

-D+T

IT HAD A LITTLE COLT (COLD)

GOOD DAYS—BAD DAYS

3.

What do insects do on Sunday?

○○○○○○○○ GO○FOR○A○BUGGY○RIDE ○○○○○○○○

What should you feed an elephant on?

TUESDAYS (2'sDAYS)

What's the best day for making pancakes?

FRIDAY (FRY-DAY)

What did the calculator say to the math teacher?

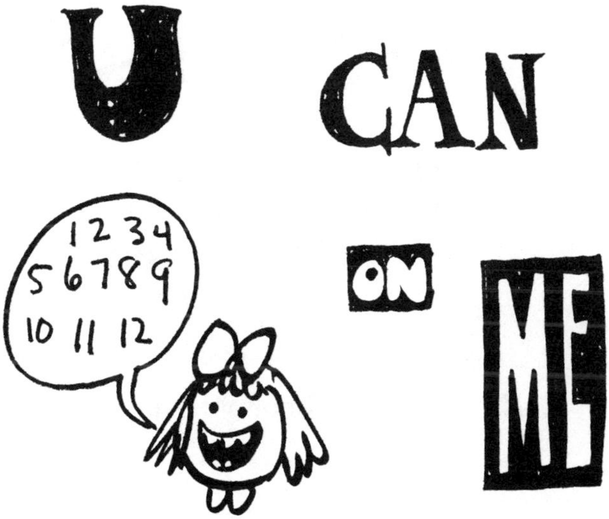
U
CAN
1 2 3 4
5 6 7 8 9
10 11 12
ON
ME

"YOU CAN COUNT ON ME!"

Where do you put money for a rainy day?

N
a
-r+k

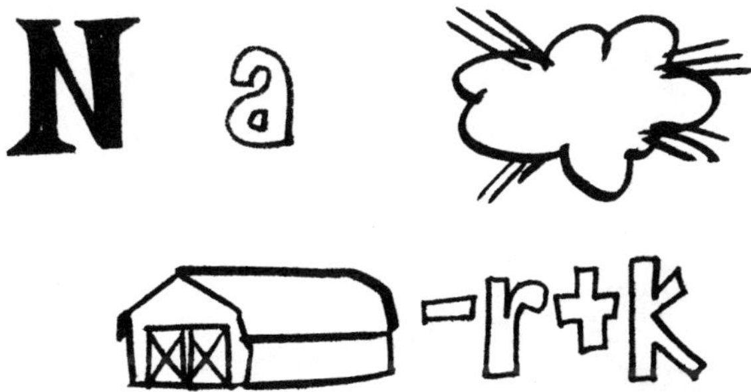

IN A CLOUD BANK

HOW'S BUSINESS?

THIS IS A MATCH-UP. JUST PUT THE RIDDLES (ON THIS PAGE) TOGETHER WITH THE BEST ANSWERS (THEY'RE OUT OF ORDER) ON THE NEXT PAGE.

1. How is the astronomy business?

2. How is the electric light business?

3. How is the dress-making business?

4. How is the rodeo business?

5. How is the submarine business?

A.

B.

C.

D.

E.

1. C (LOOKING UP)
2. E (OFF AND ON)
3. D (SEW-SEW) (SO-SO)
4. B (FALLING OFF)
5. A (GOING UNDER)

What did Mrs. Claus say to Santa when she heard a patter on the roof?

"IT SOUNDS LIKE RAIN, DEAR (REINDEER)."

SLURPS & BURPS

4.

What's worse than finding a worm in the apple you're eating?

FINDING HALF A WORM

What looks like half a pumpkin?

THE OTHER HALF

What has hands but never washes them?

A CLOCK

What's useless unless it's in a tight spot?

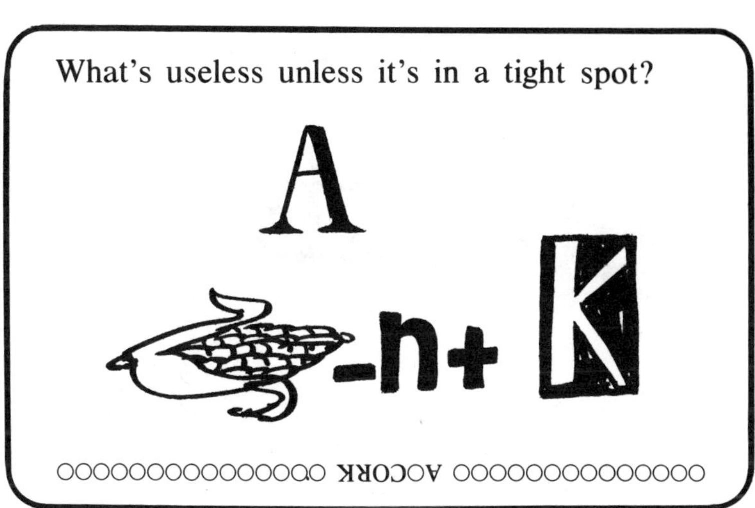

A CORK

What is purple or white and has its heart in its head?

A CABBAGE

What always gets served but never gets eaten?

TENNIS BALLS

How do you make a lemon drop?

LET IT FALL

How do you eat soup with a fork?

VERY SLOWLY

What cranky violinist do you find on the beach?

A FIDDLER CRAB

CRAZY QUESTIONS

1. 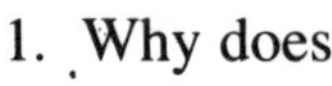Why does  shock people?
2. How can you recognize  stew?
3. How do you scold an  ?
4. What did the sugar say to the  ?
5. Why was the running along the cereal box?

IN A CRAZY QUESTION THE RIDDLE HAS A PICTURE IN IT. YOU NEED TO FIGURE OUT THE RIDDLE QUESTION FIRST AND THEN MATCH IT UP WITH THE ANSWERS (THAT ARE ALL OUT OF ORDER) BELOW.

A. Say "Tusk-Tusk!"

B. It said, "Tear along the dotted line."

C. "I'm sweet, but don't stir me up!"

D. It doesn't know how to conduct itself.

E. By the hares in it.

1. ○○ D (IT DOESN'T KNOW HOW TO CONDUCT ITSELF) ○○
2. ○○○○○○○○ E (BY THE HARES IN IT) ○○○○○○○○
3. ○○○○○○○ A (SAY "TUSK-TUSK!") ○○○○○○○
4. ○ C ("I'M SWEET, BUT DON'T STIR ME UP!") ○
5. ○ B (IT SAID, "TEAR ALONG THE DOTTED LINE.") ○

When is it polite to serve milk in a saucer?

THE

WHEN YOU FEED THE CAT

SNEEZES & WHEEZES

5.

If your nose runs and your feet smell, what's wrong with you?

YOU'RE BUILT UPSIDE DOWN

What letter can make you sick?

V. IT'S ALWAYS IN LOVE

What is a sure cure for dandruff?

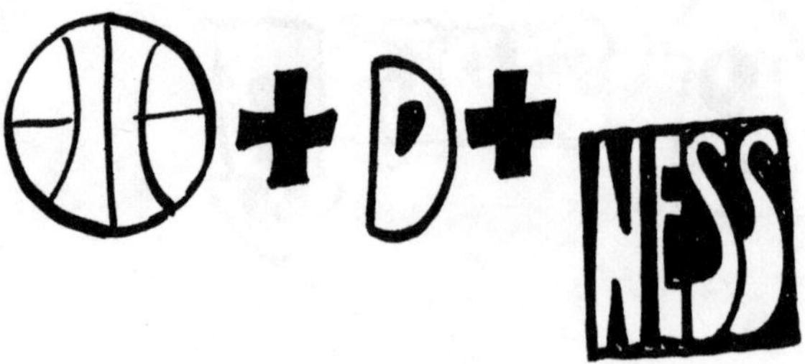

BALDNESS

How can you stop a sleepwalker from walking in his sleep?

KEEP HIM AWAKE

How can you go ten days without sleep and not be tired?

SLEEP NIGHTS

MATCH UP THE RIDDLES (ON THIS PAGE) WITH THEIR ANSWERS (THEY'RE OUT OF ORDER) ON THE NEXT PAGE.

1. What has pains but no aches?

2. What has a head, and four legs, but only one foot?

3. What can a man be that a woman can't?

4. What never blinks when you stick something in its eye?

5. What has a head and a tail, but no body?

A.

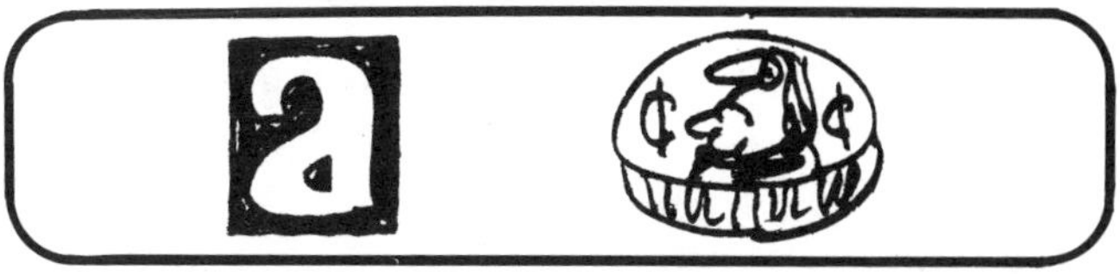

B.

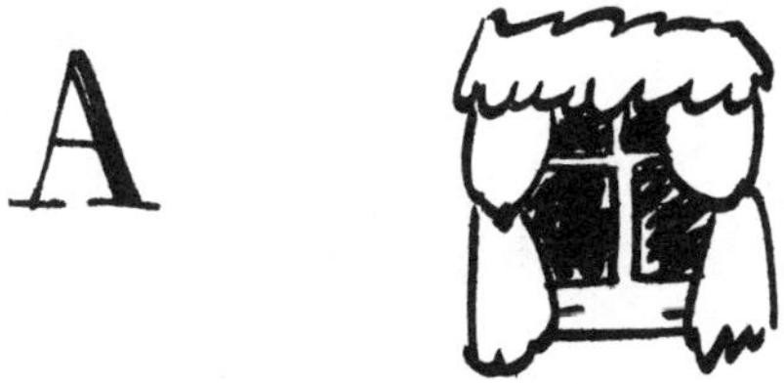

C.

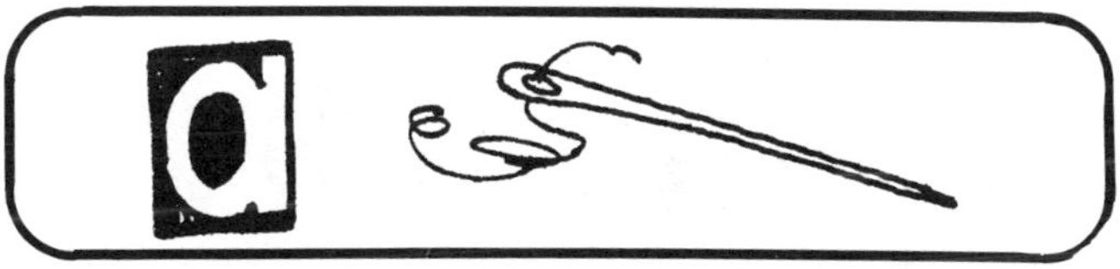

D.

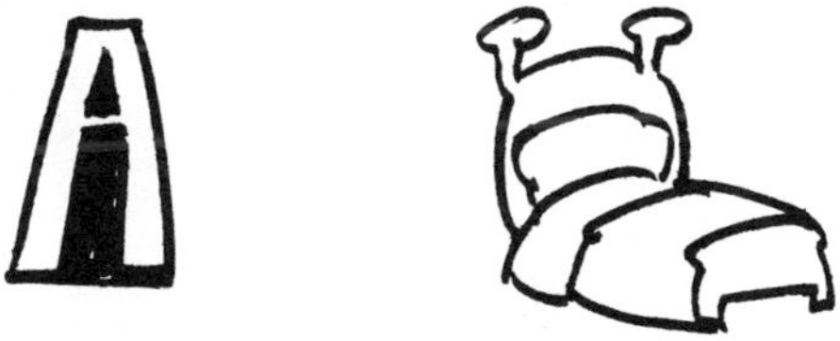

E.

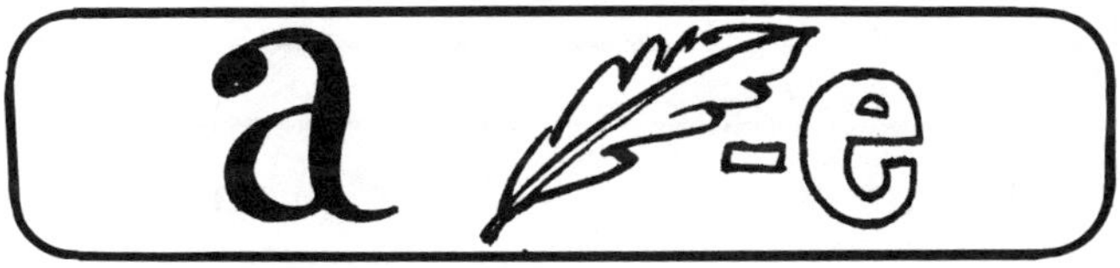

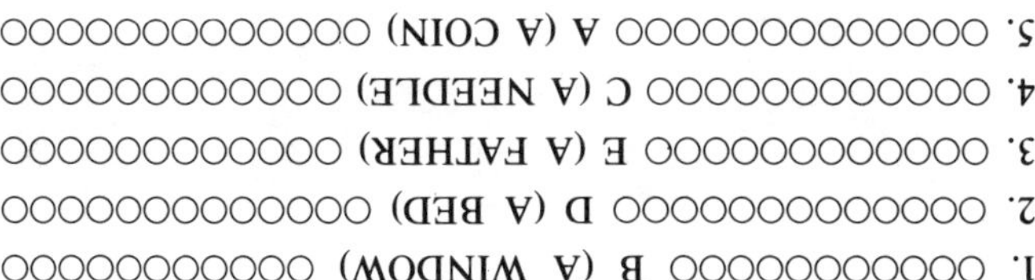

1. OOOOOOOOOOO B (A WINDOW) OOOOOOOOOOOO
2. OOOOOOOOOOOOOO D (A BED) OOOOOOOOOOOOOO
3. OOOOOOOOOOOOO E (A FATHER) OOOOOOOOOOOOO
4. OOOOOOOOOOOOO C (A NEEDLE) OOOOOOOOOOOOO
5. OOOOOOOOOOOOOOO A (A COIN) OOOOOOOOOOOOOOO

How do you drive a baby buggy?

OOOOOOOO TAKE○AWAY○ITS○RATTLE OOOOOOOO

If your nose was on strike, what would you do?

OOOOOOOOOO PICKET○(PICK○IT) OOOOOOOOOOOOO

FOWL PLAY

6.

What did the baby chick say when the hen laid an orange?

O, C THE

MAR + ma + laid!

"OH, SEE THE ORANGE MARMALADE (LAID)!"

What bird looks most like a stork?

ANOTHER STORK

How can you keep a rooster from crowing on Monday?

EAT HIM ON SUNDAY

What did the chicken say to the rooster?

LET me -B+E

"LET ME USE YOUR COMB"

What happened when the hen swallowed a yo-yo?

SHE LAID THE SAME EGG THREE TIMES

MATCH-UPS

MATCH UP THE RIDDLES (ON THIS PAGE) WITH THEIR ANSWERS (THEY'RE OUT OF ORDER) ON THE NEXT PAGE.

1. Where do giant condors come from?

2. If an egg comes floating down the river, where does it come from?

3. What becomes more valuable when it's used up?

4. What grows up as it grows down?

5. What's the best thing for hives?

A.

B.

C.

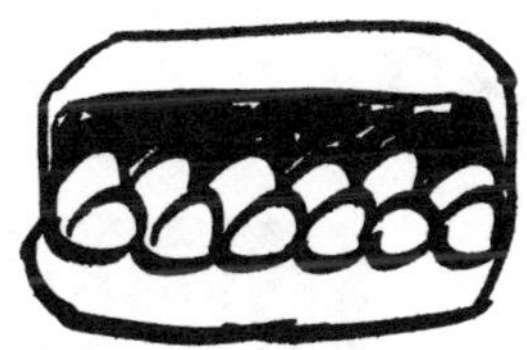

D.

E.

1. C (EGGS)
2. D (A CHICKEN)
3. E (AN UMBRELLA)
4. A (A GOOSE)
5. B (BEES)

Why does a chicken lay an egg?

MOVING RIGHT ALONG . . .

7.

What has three feet but can't walk?

A YARDSTICK

What part of New York is in Chicago?

OOOOOOOOOOOOO THE○LETTER○O OOOOOOOOOOOO

How can you make O move?

OOOOOOO PUT○A○GO○IN○FRONT○OF○IT OOOOOOO

What is the hardest key to turn?

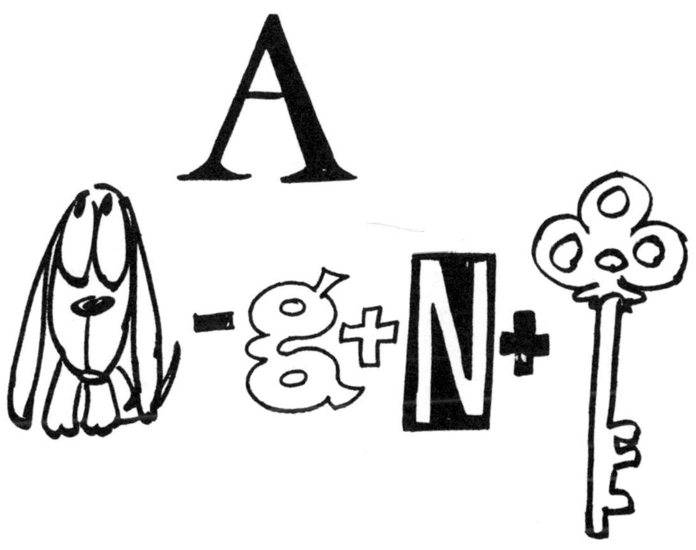

OOOOOOOOOOOOOO AODONKEY OOOOOOOOOOOOOO

What has sleeves and is put on wet?

OOOOOOOOOO AOCOATOOFOPAINT OOOOOOOOOO

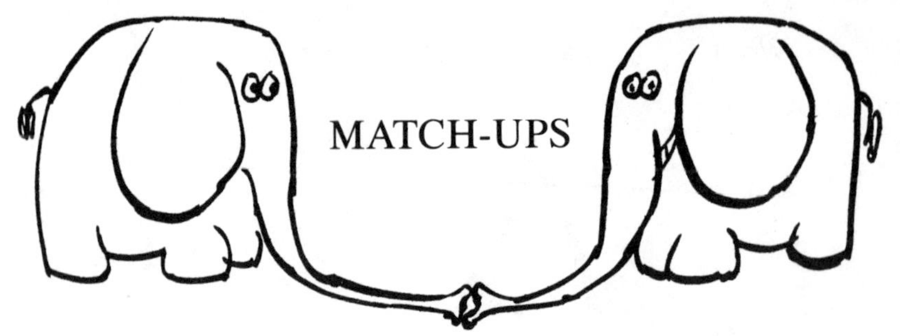

MATCH UP THE RIDDLES (ON THIS PAGE) WITH THEIR ANSWERS (THEY'RE OUT OF ORDER) ON THE NEXT PAGE.

1. What kind of room has no walls?

2. What always enters the house through the keyhole?

3. What is both inside and outside the house—yet in its place?

4. The English alphabet goes from A to Z. What goes from Z to A?

5. What does a poor man have—that a rich man wants?

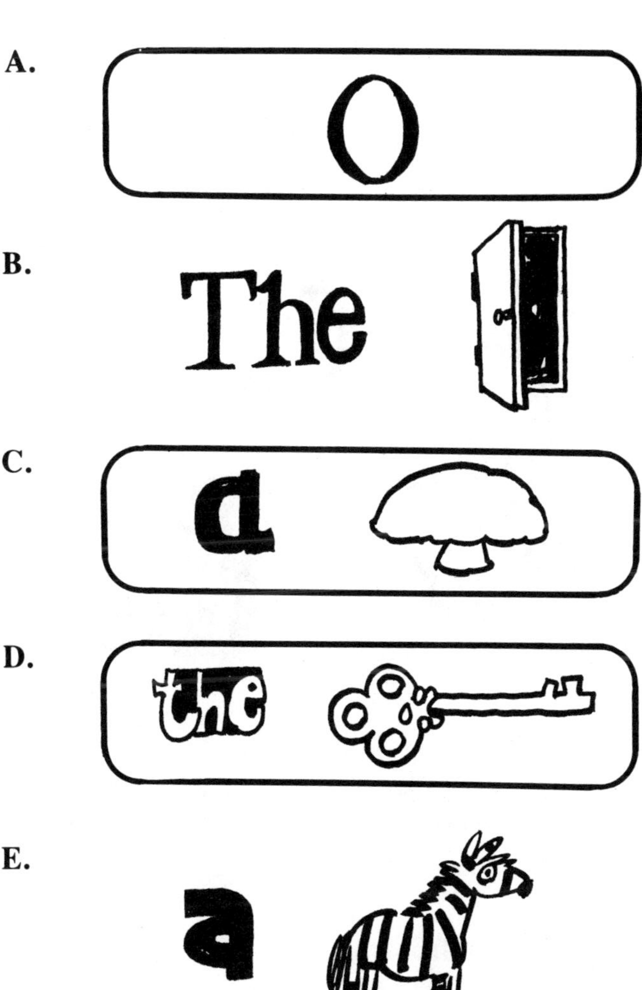

1. C (A MUSHROOM)
2. D (THE KEY)
3. B (THE DOOR)
4. E (A ZEBRA)
5. A (NOTHING)

When General Lee fell off his horse, which way was he going?

DOWN

How do you get from here to there?

$$\begin{array}{r} 1 \\ +2 \\ +3 \\ +2 \\ \hline =8 \end{array}$$

T

ADDOT

I never ask questions, but I demand many answers. What am I?

A DOORBELL

Where was Noah when the lights went out?

IN THE DARK

What has a hundred legs, but can't walk?

50 PAIRS OF PANTS

What runs in and out of town—day and night?

THE

r+

I AM NOT A FROG

T

THE ROAD

Why is a large coat like a banana peel?

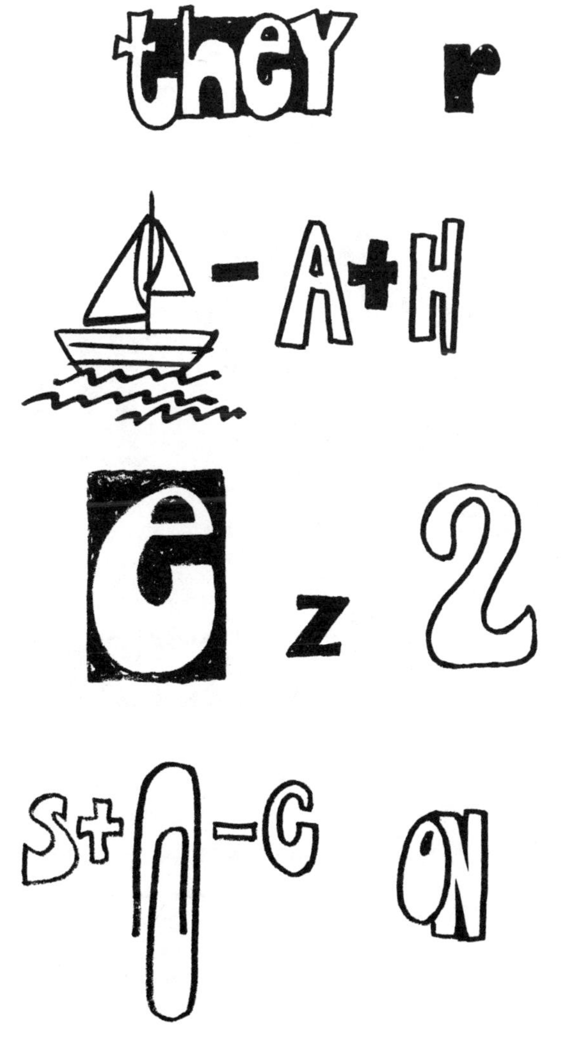

○○○ THEY○ARE○BOTH○EASY○TO○SLIP○ON ○○○

What was the turtle doing on the freeway?

HALF A MILE AN HOUR

BAD LUCK!

8.

How do you keep a skunk from smelling?

H +

its

○○○○○○○○○○○○ HOLD○ITS○NOSE ○○○○○○○○○○○○

What do you get if you cross a skunk and a porcupine?

A SMELLY PINCUSHION

How did the mouse get a short tail?

CATNIP

When the dinosaur fell in the swimming pool, how did it get out?

WET

What has 50 heads, but no brains?

A BOOK OF MATCHES

What makes the cemetery so noisy?

-B the

-ee+ iN

ALL THE COUGHIN' (COFFIN)

Why are banks noisy?

MONEY TALKS

What has two tongues and no mouth?

A PAIR OF SHOES

When is it good to lose your temper?

W+

its

A

-L

1

WHEN IT'S A BAD ONE

CRAZY QUESTIONS

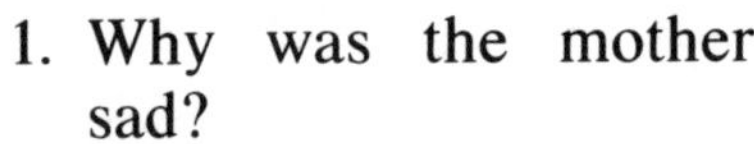

1. Why was the mother sad?

2. What kind of makes you move faster?

3. What goes from New York to iANROFILAC without moving?

4. What's worse than raining and ?

5. Where do you find ?

IN A CRAZY QUESTION THE RIDDLE HAS A PICTURE IN IT. YOU NEED TO FIGURE OUT THE RIDDLE QUESTION FIRST AND THEN MATCH IT UP WITH THE ANSWERS (THAT ARE ALL OUT OF ORDER) BELOW.

A. Hailing buses.

B. Railroad tracks.

C. Where you lost them.

D. All her children had gone to the dogs.

E. A hurricane.

1. OO FLEA—D (ALL HER CHILDREN HAD GONE OO OOOOOOOOOOOO TO THE DOGS) OOOOOOOOOOOOO
2. OOOOOOOO CANE—E (A HURRICANE) OOOOOOOOO
3. OOOO CALIFORNIA—B (RAILROAD TRACKS) OOOO
4. OOOOO CATS/DOGS—A (HAILING BUSES) OOOOO
5. OOOO TIGERS—C (WHERE YOU LOST THEM) OOOO

What must an astronaut do before he gets out of his space suit?

GET INTO IT

Why shouldn't you swim on an empty stomach?

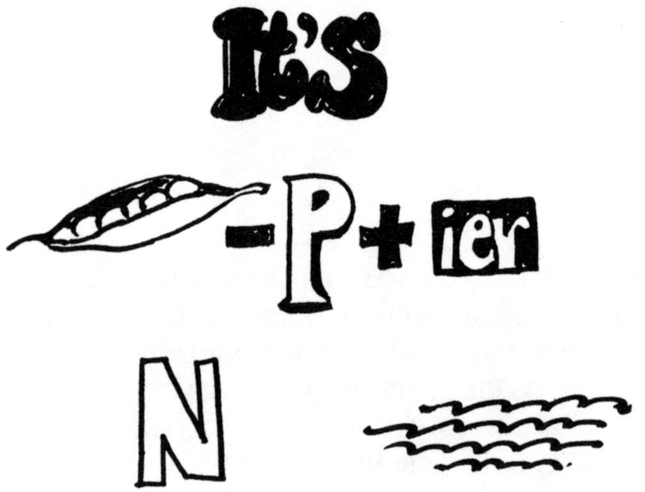

IT'S EASIER IN WATER

When is a donkey not a donkey?

WHEN IT'S A LITTLE HOARSE (HORSE)

Why did Myrtle wave her hair?

½

SHE DIDN'T HAVE A FLAG

FUN & GAMES

9.

What did the mad magician pull out of his hat?

○○○○○○○○○○○ HIS○HARE○(HAIR) ○○○○○○○○○○○

Why do bad mice run faster than good mice?

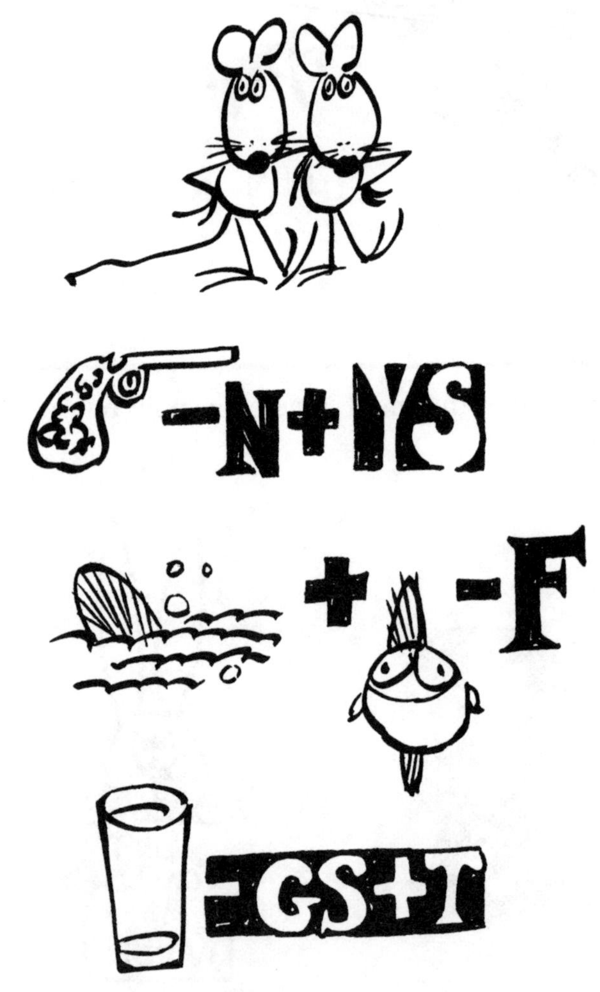

○○○○○ MICE○(NICE)○GUYS○FINISH○LAST ○○○○○

When mice go jogging, what do they wear?

SQ+
-SN

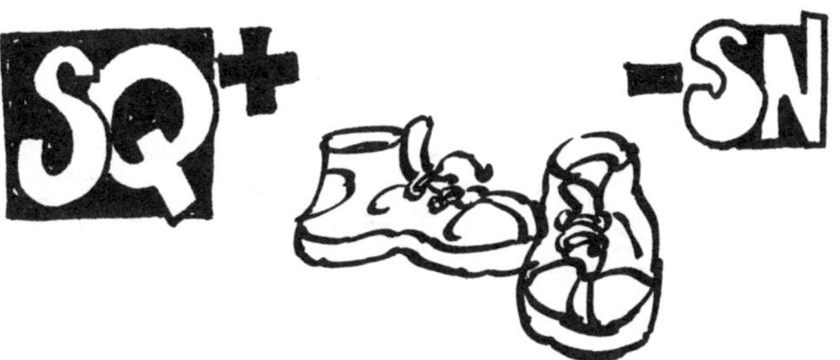

SQUEAKERS (SNEAKERS)

Why is R always a winner?

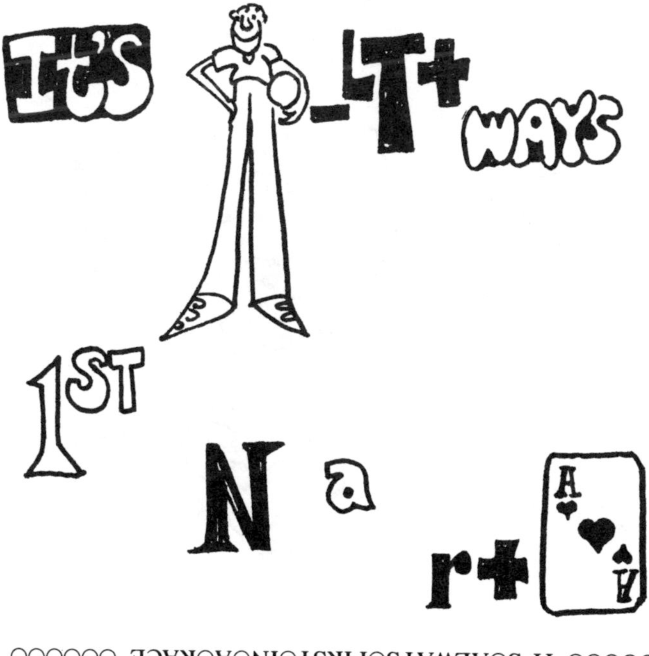
It's
-LT+
WAYS
1ST
N
a
r+
A

IT'S ALWAYS FIRST IN A RACE

What kind of paper makes the best kite?

FLY PAPER

Why did the baseball coach put a spider on the team?

TOO CATCH FLIES

What can you hold in your left hand but not in your right?

YOUR RIGHT ELBOW

Can you row?

YES, CAN YOU (CANOE)?

CRAZY QUESTIONS

1. Did you ever see a bake?

2. Did you ever see a drawer?

3. Did you ever see a  shake?

4. Did you ever see a smoke?

5. Did you ever see a punch?

IN A CRAZY QUESTION THE RIDDLE HAS A PICTURE IN IT. YOU NEED TO FIGURE OUT THE RIDDLE QUESTION FIRST AND THEN MATCH IT UP WITH THE ANSWERS (THAT ARE ALL OUT OF ORDER) BELOW.

A. No, but I've seen an engine puff.

B. No, but I've seen an apple turnover.

C. No, but I've seen a base hit.

D. No, but I've seen greasepaint.

E. No, but I've seen an oyster stew.

1. CLAM—E (NO, BUT I'VE SEEN AN OYSTER STEW)
2. DRESSER—D (NO, BUT I'VE SEEN GREASEPAINT)
3. STRAWBERRY—B (NO, BUT I'VE SEEN AN APPLE TURNOVER)
4. CHIMNEY—A (NO, BUT I'VE SEEN AN ENGINE PUFF)
5. FRUIT—C (NO, BUT I'VE SEEN A BASE HIT)

How did the girl octopus and the boy octopus come aboard Noah's Ark?

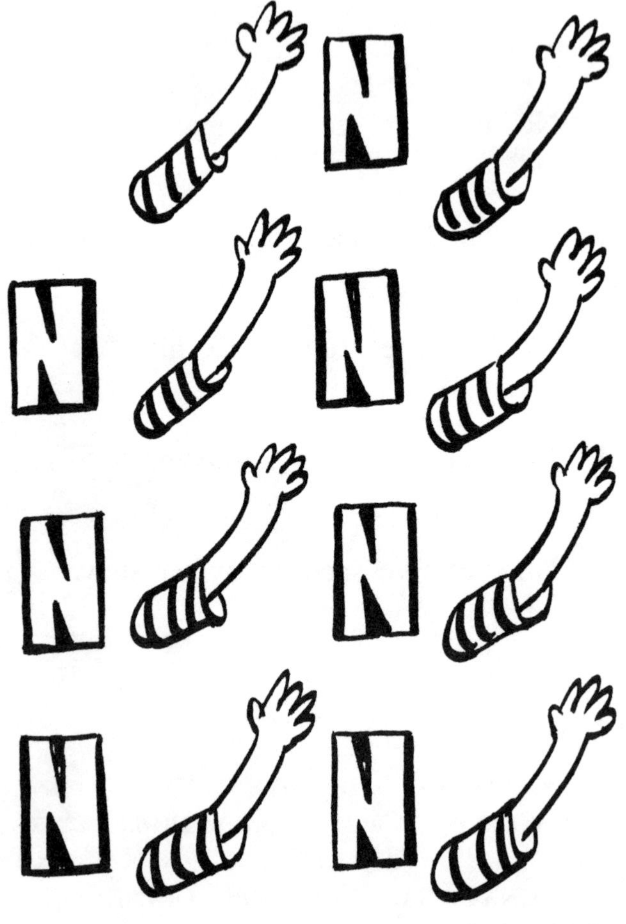

OO ARMOINOARMOINOARMOINOARMOINOARM OO

OOOOOOOO INOARMOINOARMOINOARM OOOOOOOO

PLAYING IT SAFE

10.

What has eight feet, four heads and sings?

A QUARTET

What did the hornplayer say to the drummer?

"BEAT IT!"

What did the drummer say to the hornplayer?

"I DON'T GIVE A TOOT."

What did the hornplayer say to the violinist?

DON'T

-r

around

-G

ME

"DON'T FIDDLE AROUND WITH ME!"

What did the piano player say to the violinist?

"I FORGOT MY KEYS."

What did the composer say to the harpist?

"DON'T STRING ME ALONG!"

What did the harpist say to the composer?

"NOTES (NUTS) TO YOU!"

What do you call ten stones with electric guitars?

A ROCK GROUP

What kind of musical group makes no sound?

A RUBBER BAND

CRAZY QUESTIONS

1. Why don't mice answer the  ?

2. How does a  get rid of his customers?

3. How can you  and not get hurt?

4. What did the  sing to the  ?

5. Why did the  spit up Jonah?

IN A CRAZY QUESTION THE RIDDLE HAS A PICTURE IN IT. YOU NEED TO FIGURE OUT THE RIDDLE QUESTION FIRST AND THEN MATCH IT UP WITH THE ANSWERS (THAT ARE ALL OUT OF ORDER) BELOW.

A. "There will never be another ewe."

B. Jump out of a basement window.

C. Because no mews is good mews.

D. You can't keep a good man down.

E. He gives them the brush.

1. ○○ TELEPHONE—C○(BECAUSE○NO○MEWS○IS ○○
○○○○○○○○○○○○ GOOD○MEWS) ○○○○○○○○○○○○
2. ○ BARBER—E○(HE○GIVES○THEM○THE○BRUSH)
3. ○○○○○ JUMP○OUT○OF○A○WINDOW— ○○○○○○
○○ B○(JUMP○OUT○OF○A○BASEMENT○WINDOW) ○○
4. ○ BOY○SHEEP/GIRL○SHEEP—A○("THERE○WILL ○
○○○○○○ NEVER○BE○ANOTHER○EWE.") ○○○○○○○
5. ○○○○ WHALE—D○(YOU○CAN'T○KEEP○A ○○○○○
○○○○○○○○○○ GOOD○MAN○DOWN) ○○○○○○○○○○○

What do singers always take before singing?

○○○○○○○○○○○ A○DEEP○BREATH ○○○○○○○○○○○

CELEBRITY RIDDLES

11.

What game did Dr. Jekyll like to play?

○○○○○ HYDE-AND-SICK○(HIDE-AND-SEEK) ○○○○○

What does everyone have that Adam and Eve didn't have?

PARENTS

At what time of day was Adam created?

A LITTLE BEFORE EVE

When did queens carry large umbrellas?

○○○○○ WHEN○KINGS○REIGNED○(RAINED) ○○○○○

Where are kings usually crowned?

○○○○○○○○○○○○○ ON○THE○HEAD ○○○○○○○○○○○○○

Why don't radishes disagree with Muhammad Ali?

THEY WOULDN'T DARE

Why was Grant buried in Grant's tomb?

○○○○○○○○○○○○○ HE○WAS○DEAD ○○○○○○○○○○○○

What did you see when Merlin set off the fireworks?

A FLYING SORCERER

HOW BEASTLY!

12.

How can you tell an elephant from an absent-minded professor?

THE ELEPHANT REMEMBERS

Why do tigers lie down?

OOOOOOOOOO THEY CAN'T LIE UP OOOOOOOOOO

Why do tigers eat raw meat?

THEY

C+ -P

C+ -B

OOOOOOOOOO THEY CAN'T COOK OOOOOOOOOO

Why are leopards spotted?

-G+M

SCRATCH
SCRATCH

○○ SO○YOU○CAN○TELL○THEM○FROM○FLEAS ○○

What time is it when a monkey scratches a flea?

○○○○○○○○○○ FIVE○AFTER○ONE ○○○○○○○○○○○○

How did the gorilla get out of its cage?

OOOOO WITH○A○MONKEY○(A○MONK○KEY) OOOOO

What should you do if you find a gorilla asleep in your bed?

OOOOOOOO SLEEP○SOMEWHERE○ELSE OOOOOOOO

Why does a woolly sheep scratch himself?

HE HAS FLEAS (FLEECE)

On which side does a bear have fur?

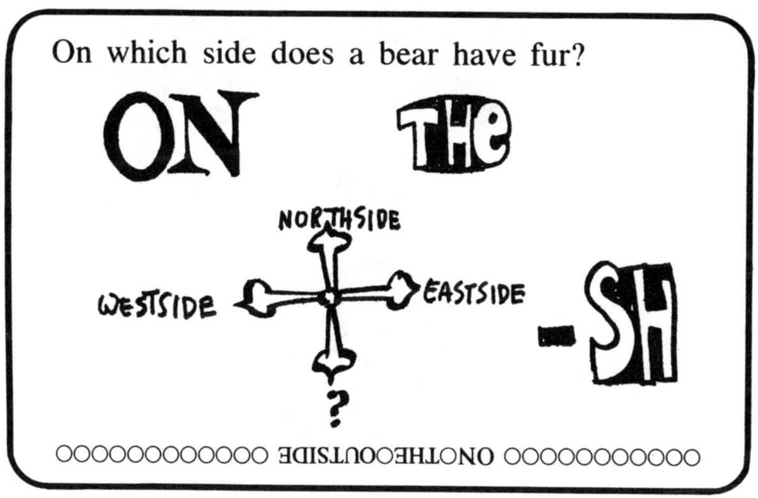

ON THE OUTSIDE

CRAZY QUESTIONS

1. How do you get fur from a ?

2. What did the say to the ?

3. When is a  not a  ?

4. What should you do if you see an angry  ?

5. How does an  get up an oak tree?

IN A CRAZY QUESTION THE RIDDLE HAS A PICTURE IN IT. YOU NEED TO FIGURE OUT THE RIDDLE QUESTION FIRST AND THEN MATCH IT UP WITH THE ANSWERS (THAT ARE ALL OUT OF ORDER) BELOW.

A. When it's lion (lying) down.

B. Hope it doesn't see you.

C. "It's been nice gnawing (knowing) you."

D. He climbs on an acorn and waits.

E. Climb a tree.

1.○○○○○○○ BEAR—E○(CLIMB○A○TREE) ○○○○○○○
2.○○○○○○○○○○○ BEAVER/TREE— ○○○○○○○○○○○
○○○ C○("IT'S○BEEN○NICE○GNAWING○YOU") ○○○○
3.○○ TIGER/TIGER—A○(WHEN○IT'S○LION○DOWN) ○
4.○○○○○○○○○○○○ RHINOCEROS—○○○○○○○○○○○○
○○○○○ B○(HOPE○IT○DOESN'T○SEE○YOU) ○○○○○○
5.○○○○ ELEPHANT—D○(HE○CLIMBS○ON○AN ○○○○
○○○○○○○○○○○ ACORN○AND○WAITS) ○○○○○○○○○○

What did Papa Gnu say to Mama Gnu when Baby Gnu was naughty?

"GO PADDLE YOUR OWN GNU"

MAD MENAGERIE

13.

What does a farmer say when you tell him a joke?

OOOOOOOO HO-HO-HOO(HOE-HOE-HOE) OOOOOOOO

How do pigs write?

WITH A PIG PEN

What do bees do with their honey?

CELL IT (SELL IT)

How do you make wild corn behave?

○○○○○○○○○○○○○ BOX○ITS○EARS ○○○○○○○○○○○○○

Where do little ears of corn come from?

○○○○ THE○STORK○(STALK)○BRINGS○THEM ○○○○

Why did the farmer stand behind the donkey?

HE THOUGHT HE'D GET A KICK OUT OF IT

Why don't farmers milk their mice?

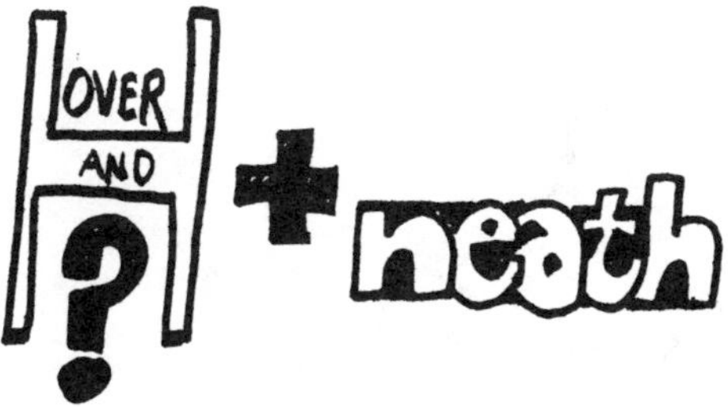

○○ THEY○CAN'T○GET○TO○THE○PAIL○UNDERNEATH ○

Why is a goose like a cow's tail?

THEY BOTH GROW DOWN

What is smaller than a flea's mouth?

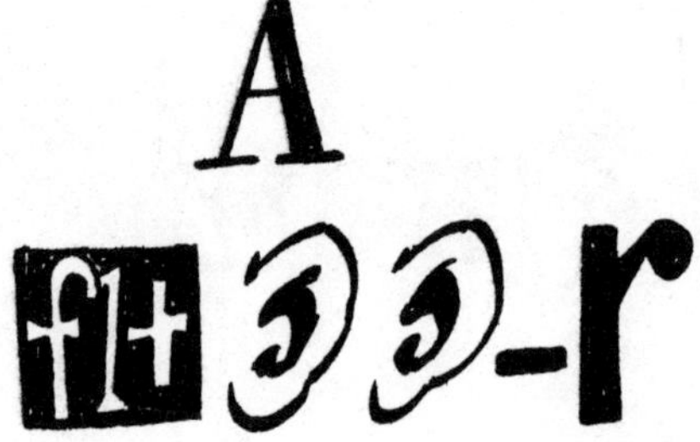

A FLEA'S LIPS

What did the dog do at the flea circus?

HE STOLE THE SHOW

Why does a dog wag his tail?

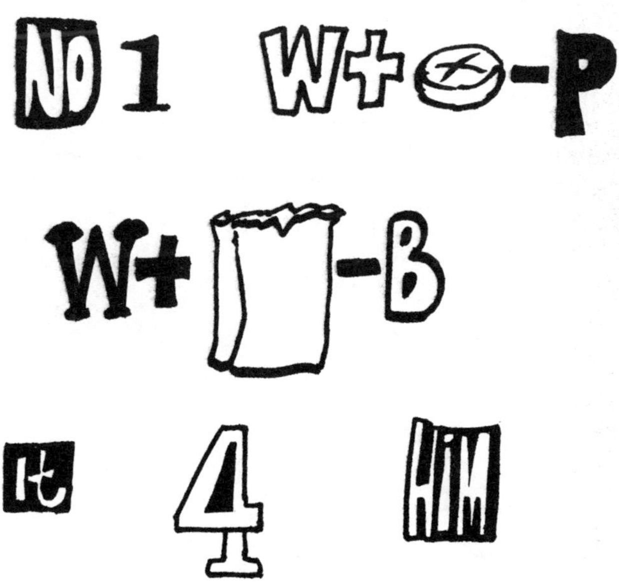

NO 1 W+ -P

W+ -B

it 4 HiM

NO ONE WILL WAG IT FOR HIM

What did the cat see in the desert on Christmas Eve?

SANDY CLAWS (SANTA CLAUS)

What did the bee say to the sheep on Christmas Day?

"BAH! HUMBUG!"

Why is a cat on a fence like a coin?

IT HAS A HEAD ON ONE SIDE, A TAIL ON THE OTHER

What has four heads, four tails and smells?

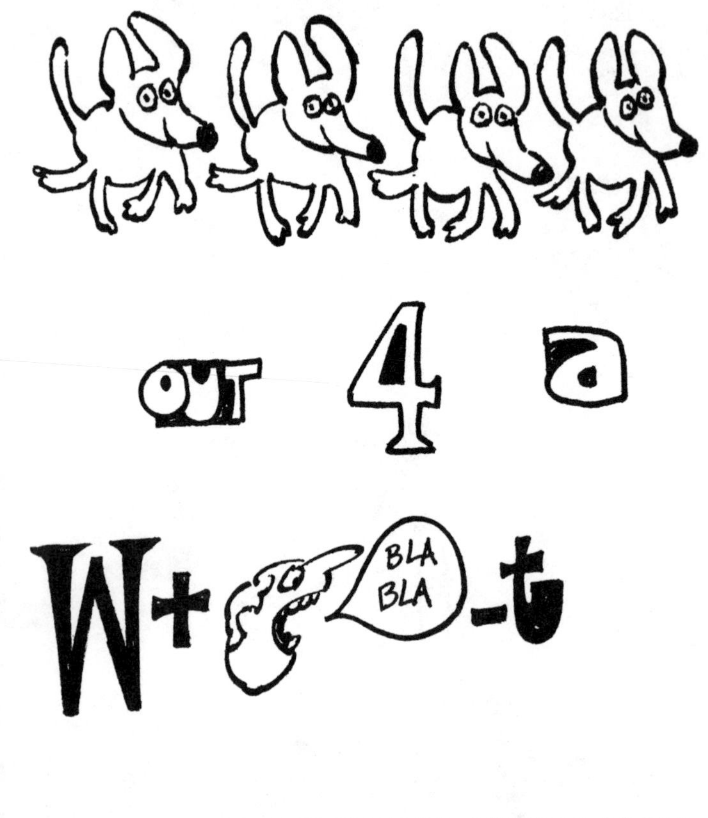

FOUR DOGS OUT FOR A WALK

GRAB BAG

14.

What does someone else have to take before you get it?

YOUR PICTURE

How do you make a cigarette lighter?

TAKE○OUT○THE○TOBACCO

What can write blue, red, green, orange, yellow and black?

A○PENCIL

What can you give someone and still keep?

YOUR WORD

What can you break with one word?

SILENCE

How much dirt is there in a hole two feet deep and one foot across?

OOOOOOOOOOOOOOOO NONE OOOOOOOOOOOOOOOO

What falls down all the time, but never gets hurt?

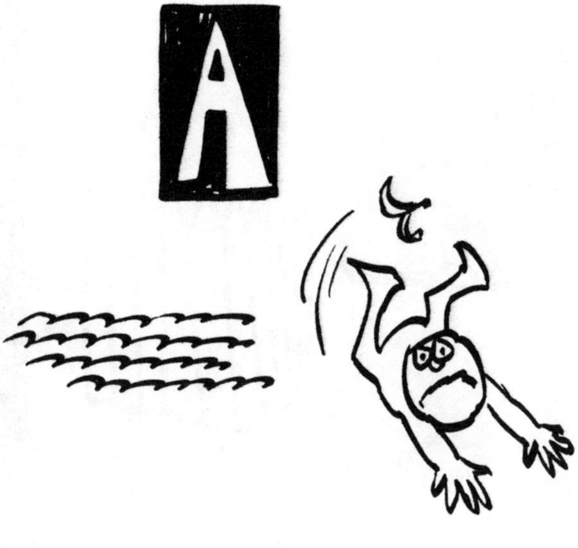

OOOOOOOOOOOO A WATERFALL OOOOOOOOOOOO

How do you turn a 30-piece set of dishes into a 300-piece set?

DROP IT

What happens if the rain keeps up?

IT WON'T COME DOWN

CRAZY QUESTIONS

1. What has a but never speaks and a bed but never ?

2. What kind of do you use in math class?

3. Why couldn't they play cards on the ?

4. Why do you put the right on first?

5. What did the say to the jeweler?

IN A CRAZY QUESTION THE RIDDLE HAS A PICTURE IN IT. YOU NEED TO FIGURE OUT THE RIDDLE QUESTION FIRST AND THEN MATCH IT UP WITH THE ANSWERS (THAT ARE ALL OUT OF ORDER) BELOW.

A. It's silly to put on the wrong one.

B. "Give me a ring sometime."

C. A river.

D. Because Noah sat on the deck.

E. Multipliers.

1. OOOOOO MOUTH/SLEEPS—C (A RIVER) OOOOOO
2. OOOOOOO PLIERS—E (MULTIPLIERS) OOOOOOO
3. O ARK—D (BECAUSE NOAH SAT ON THE DECK) O
4. O SHOE—A (IT'S SILLY TO PUT ON THE WRONG ONE) O
5. O BATHTUB—B ("GIVE ME A RING SOMETIME") O

If Harold wears his pants out before noon, what should he do?

WEAR THEM BACK IN

TOUGHIES

15.

Why do white sheep eat more than black sheep?

OOOOOOO THERE○ARE○MORE○OF○THEM OOOOOOO

What did the dandelion say to the flower bed?

TAKE ME TO YOUR WEEDER

Would you help a lady in distress?

'D

SL+P

a

in

NE

I'D HELP A LADY IN ANY DRESS

What did the big toe say to the little toe?

OOOOO "THERE'S A HEEL FOLLOWING US." OOOOO

When does a horse see as much from behind as in front?

WHEN IT'S EYES ARE CLOSED

Why does a dog chase its tail?

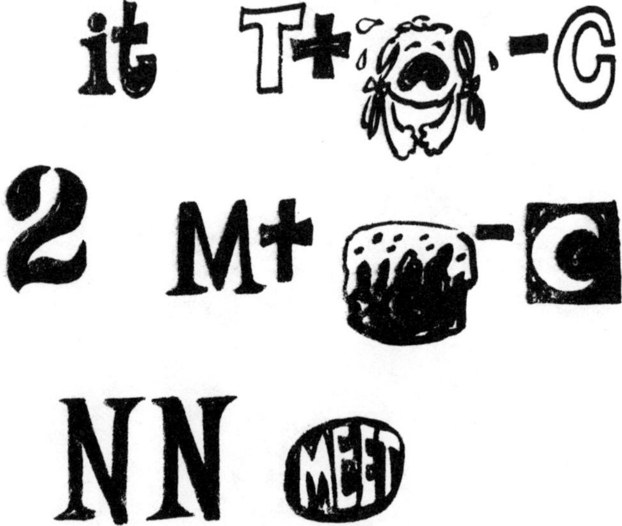

IT TRIES TO MAKE ENDS (NNs) MEET

How can you swallow a door without choking?

B+ -GA+T

it

D+ -CL

BOLT IT DOWN

Which snake is best at arithmetic?

3
+2
+5
+7
+8

THE ADDER

Why was the baby goat angry at its parents?

THEY TREATED IT LIKE A KID

Why do bulls charge?

THEY SELDOM CARRY CASH

Why is Q impolite?

OOOO IT ALWAYS GOES AHEAD OF YOU (U) OOOO

How many legs does a race horse have?

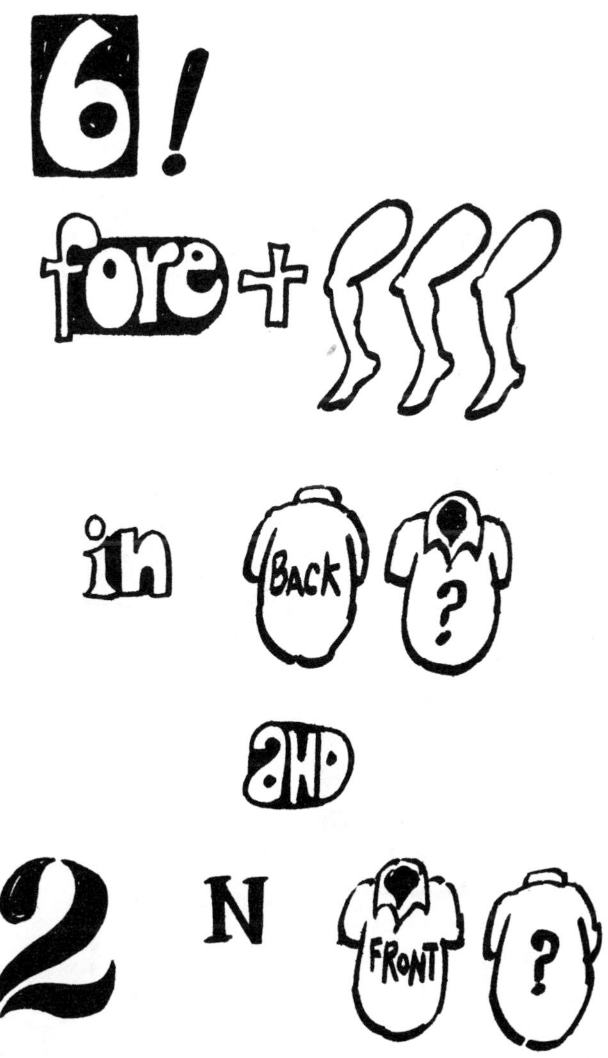

SIX! FOUR (FORE) LEGS IN FRONT AND TWO IN BACK

Why was the Joker wild?

HE

-h+n't

PLAYING

-C

a

HE WASN'T PLAYING WITH A FULL DECK

Why is a long road like a cat's tail?

IT'S FUR (FAR) TO THE END

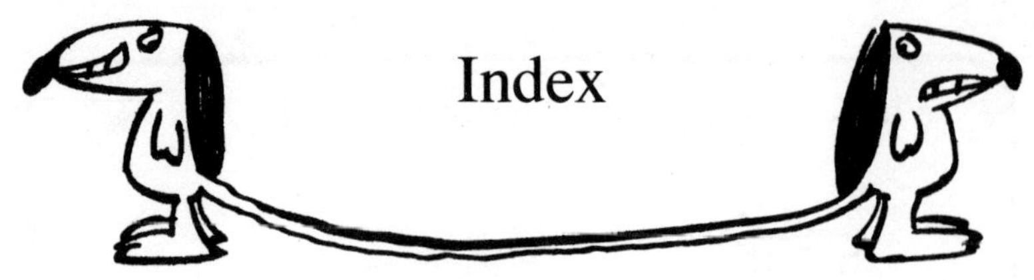

Index